Independent Voices

EVE MERRIAM

Independent

Voices

drawings by Arvis Stewart

ATHENEUM   1968   New York

COPYRIGHT © 1968 BY EVE MERRIAM
ALL RIGHTS RESERVED
LIBRARY OF CONGRESS CATALOG CARD NUMBER 68-18453
PUBLISHED SIMULTANEOUSLY IN CANADA BY
MCCLELLAND & STEWART LTD.
MANUFACTURED IN THE UNITED STATES OF AMERICA BY
KINGSPORT PRESS, INC., KINGSPORT, TENNESSEE
DESIGNED BY JUDITH LERNER
FIRST PRINTING

for

DEBORAH & JONOTHAN

Contents

A NOTE TO THE READER   *ix*

BENJAMIN FRANKLIN   *1*

ELIZABETH BLACKWELL   *11*

FREDERICK DOUGLASS   *19*

HENRY THOREAU   *31*

LUCRETIA MOTT   *41*

IDA B. WELLS   *55*

FIORELLO H. LAGUARDIA   *67*

A Note
to the Reader

Why, I ask myself. What made you choose—out of the vast panorama of American history—these particular heroes and heroines? What linked them in your mind? Surely there were many others who led lives as distinguished, as courageous, and in some instances engaged in deeds even more dramatic and unconventional.

How can I answer? I think perhaps I chose these men and women because they seemed to be not heroic. Unlike museum figures— stand back, keep your distance, please—they were not sternly authoritarian. They seemed approachable; I wasn't afraid of them. Perhaps the only explanation I can really offer is that these were the ones I chose to love, and love can never be entirely explained. (Will this help any in my searching out clues? Once, when I was an adolescent, I wrote a poem about some young stranger—it was myself disguised, of course—who pleaded to the world outside the boundaries of school and family: "Don't laugh at me. Love me. Tell me who I am." These voices were, I felt, human enough to respond to my long-ago cry.)

What appealed especially was their gumption—not hesitating to look and act like a fool—and the pinch of mischief along with the high purpose and morality in each of their personalities. All were drop-outs from Graceful Social Behavior Under Any and All Boring Circumstances. They were often vain, egocentric, quarrelsome. They made friends, but they also made enemies. Daring for their own times, they would be equally daring today. Perhaps even more so; that is something to ponder.

Ben, Elizabeth, Frederick, Henry, Lucretia, Ida B., Fiorello: the energy of their lives remains constantly astonishing. How did they manage to maintain such zest in youth and age, in success and adversity, illness and health?

The secret can be found, I think, in something that was said about Franklin by a French doctor who knew him well during the latter years of his life. "Franklin's most original trait, that one that would have made him unique no matter in what century he lived, was his art of living in the best fashion for himself and for others, making the most effective use of all the tools nature has placed at the disposal of man. He would eat, sleep, work whenever he saw fit, according to his needs, so that there never was a more leisurely man, though he certainly handled a tremendous amount of business . . ." Those words could, I believe, fit any of the other men and women in this book.

To live in the best fashion for oneself and for others; to stretch to the seeming limit of capacity and then discover further unused powers; all these cantankerous figures shared such excellence in common.

Certain of these portraits are presented fairly full face; some three-quarters turned or profile; some may seem to give the merest tantalizing glimpse. (Thoreau, for instance: his essay on Civil Disobedience and other of his great works are yet to come. Elizabeth

Blackwell is seen only at her initial triumph; physical handicaps and public hostility on a grander scale are still in the future.) One of my hopes is that these portraits will lead the reader to seek out more about these seven in history books, in biographies and autobiographies, in letters and speeches and documents of the times.

The portraits are in verse, yet no instance has any "poetic license" been taken. Every incident and description, to the best of my knowledge, is based upon true happening and not hearsay.

But if that is so, if the sketches are in no way fictionalized, then why not have presented them in factual prose? Because I felt that through the condensation and heightened speech of verse, history might come more alive and these actual independent voices might resound once again—lively, familiar, ringing clear.

The portraits can be read silently, but they are intended primarily to be read aloud. In a comfortable chair, in the company of friends, or in a classroom. In school assemblies, I hope, with a few simple props and costumes. With chorus voices representing a counterpoint to the principal speakers. (Without any cues on the printed page, it will be evident, I think, where differing voices enter in.) Certain sections of some of the poems may seem to call for music—either background atmosphere; or songs at the center stage. But that is all for your own individual voice to decide.

Independent Voices

Benjamin
Franklin

Every day, every day
young Ben could be found
hard at work
on the same old round.
Every day, every day—
working without pay.

Couldn't protest:
what was there to say?
It was the law
that he had to stay.
(Every day, every day
like a wheel going round.)

Had to keep on
till he was twenty-one.
But that would be years
and years away—!
Run, Ben, run,
he whispered to himself,
make the break now.
So early one dawn
young Ben Franklin
was up

                              and gone.

        Knew what he was running from,
        but what he was running to?
        The wind blew cold

and he was all alone,
but he didn't even care.
He was free—on his own—
he'd land somewhere!

Runaway apprentice
from Boston town
sailed out upon a vessel
that set him down
in far Philadelphia
one autumn day.
There he stood:
a shivering
pup of a stray.

    Ben, Ben, homeless Ben,
    what could a poor boy
    go and do then?

Nothing but the clothes
he wore upon his back
and a couple of books
in a battered knapsack
and just enough pennies
to buy a loaf of bread.

    But he also had
    a brain in his head.

✳

Ben, Ben, bright young Ben,
came to live by his wits,
his spirit
and his pen.

Became Ben, big Ben, infinite Ben
who lived enough lives
for twenty men!

Printer,
      shopkeeper,
            editor,
               writer,
                  fire chief,
                     librarian,

Revolution fighter!

Became a city planner,
and Postmaster Gen.
All of these and more
and more and more
were Ben!

Musician,
        linguist,
                scientist,
                        inventor,

husband,
        papa,
                provider,
                        mentor;

Ambassador to France,
                peace treaty-maker,
                                supervisor,
                                        organizer,

mover and shaker!
With only a kite
(and courage)
and a key,
Ben proved that lightning is electricity.

A daydreamer schemer,
an on-the-go-getter,
there was always a *Ben* way
to do something better!

A planner,
a spanner,
a tinker-er,
a thinker-er,
a champion non-stopper idea hopper!

Put on your Franklin specs and
gather round the Franklin stove;
read aloud *Poor Richard's Almanac*—
it's still a treasure trove.

Early to bed and early to rise
made Ben Franklin wealthy and wise.

✳

When Ben became rich,
he still hated waste:
solid silver porringers
were not to his taste;

a wooden bowl
would serve quite as well
(so long as it was full)
and the suit he liked the best
was his plain brown wool.

With owlish eyes
and forehead high,
the sound that he hooted
was always
        WHY.

      Why not invent
      a new rocking chair
      with a fan
      that in summer
      can cool off the air?

      And why not a pick
      to reach a high shelf?
      A mechanical long arm—
      he could use one himself!

Ben, Ben, curious Ben,

Ben with a powerful
quirk
for work.

He signed his name
into history
declaring the states
independent
and free:
"We must all hang together
or surely we
will all hang separately,"
said Ben, said he.

A marvel of nature
to behold:
Ben growing older
yet never old

as his body weakened
as his mind kept strong
as his ideas kept coming
right on along. . . .

       Mmmm,
       those flying balloons that in Paris he'd seen
       might ascend to become a lunar machine—.

Or,
why does the Gulf Stream move in that way?
Perhaps one might harness the ocean some day. . . .

And,
since spending to Ben was ever a crime,
he introduced daylight *saving* time.

Now during the long bright summer days
and fall and spring
and all year round
let us sing
in praise of
the one and only
untiring
inquiring
ingenious
prodigious
protean
flowering
   bowering
     towering

prolific
  terrific

scheming
                    teeming

behemoth
brain of
BEN!

Ben,
Ben,
when will the likes of him
ever appear again?
Ben,
            Ben,
        Ben,
                the endless echoing cheer of
                            BEN . . . ! ! !

✳

Elizabeth
Blackwell

What will you do when you grow up,
nineteenth-century-young-lady?
Will you sew a fine seam and spoon dappled cream
under an apple tree shady?

Or will you be a teacher
in a dames' school
and train the little dears
by the scientific rule
that mental activity
may strain
the delicate female brain;
therefore let
the curriculum stress music, French, and especially
etiquette:
teach how to set
a truly refined banquet.
Question One:
What kind of sauce
for the fish dish,
and pickle or lemon fork?
Quickly, students,
which should it be?

Now Elizabeth Blackwell, how about you?
Seamstress or teacher, which of the two?
You know there's not much else that a girl can do.
Don't mumble, Elizabeth. Learn to raise your head.

"I'm not very nimble with a needle and thread.
"I could teach music—if I had to," she said,
"But I think I'd rather be a doctor instead."

"Is this some kind of joke?"
asked the proper menfolk.
"A woman be a doctor?
Not in our respectable day!
A doctor? An M.D.! Did you hear what she said?
She's clearly and indubitably out of her head!"

"Indeed, indeed, we are thoroughly agreed,"
hissed the ladies of society all laced in and prim,
"it's a scientific fact a doctor has to be a him.
"Yes, sir,
" 'twould be against nature
"if a doctor were a her."

Hibble hobble bibble bobble
widdle waddle wag
tsk tsk
          twit twit
                    flip flap flutter
                              mitter matter mutter

13

moan groan wail and rail
>Indecorous!
>>Revolting!!
>>>*A scandal*
>>>>A SIN
their voices pierced the air like a jabbing hat-pin.
But little miss Elizabeth wouldn't give in.

To medical schools she applied.
In vain.
And applied again
and again
and again
and one rejection offered this plan:
why not disguise herself as a man?
If she pulled back her hair, put on boots and pants,
she might attend medical lectures in France.
Although she wouldn't earn a degree,
they'd let her study anatomy.

Elizabeth refused to hide
her feminine pride.
She drew herself up tall
(all five feet one of her!)

and tried again.
And denied again.
The letters answering no
mounted like winter snow.

Until the day
when her ramrod will
finally had its way.
After the twenty-ninth try,
there came from Geneva, New York
the reply
of a blessed
Yes!

Geneva,
Geneva,
how sweet the sound;
Geneva,
Geneva,
sweet sanctuary found. . . .

. . . . and the ladies of Geneva
passing by her in the street
drew back their hoopskirts
so they wouldn't have to meet.

Psst, psst,
hiss, hiss
this sinister scarlet miss.

Avoid her, the hoyden, the hussy,
lest we all be contaminated!
If your glove so much as touch her, my dear,
best go get it fumigated!

When Elizabeth came to table,
their talking all would halt;
wouldn't so much as ask her
please to pass the salt.

In between classes
without a kind word,

Elizabeth dwelt
like a pale gray bird.

In a bare attic room
cold as a stone,
far from her family,
huddled alone

studying, studying
throughout the night
warming herself
with an inner light:

don't let it darken,
the spark of fire;
keep it aglow,
that heart's desire:

the will to serve,
to help those in pain—
flickered and flared
and flickered again—

until
like a fairy tale
(except it was true!)
Elizabeth received
her honored due.

The perfect happy ending
came to pass:
Elizabeth graduated . . .
. . . at the head of her class.

And the ladies of Geneva
all rushed forward now to greet
that clever, dear Elizabeth,
so talented, so sweet!

Wasn't it glorious
she'd won first prize?

Elizabeth smiled
with cool gray eyes

and she wrapped her shawl
against the praise:

how soon there might come
more chilling days.

Turned to leave
without hesitating.

She was ready now,
and the world was waiting.

Frederick Douglass

Women's Council.
   Washington, D.C.
      February twentieth, eighteen hundred and ninety-five.

Susan B. Anthony led him onto the platform:
a legend while he was still alive.

Prince of abolitionists,
man with the golden voice and the silver pen.
Orator, editor of the *North Star*.
Adviser to President Lincoln.
Minister to Haiti and Santo Domingo.
United States Marshal.
Titles, honors, badges too many to tabulate.
Douglass Hall named for him in Baltimore.
His statue in the University of Rochester:
a marble monument
and the man not even dead!
But he never would be,
for he was immortal Douglass,
everlasting champion
of the rights of all.

Look at him standing there,
taller than ordinary men,
still upright,
still going strong. . . .
The crowd of delegates cheered loud and long
for the giant with the flaming white hair and beard.

He looked a little like God,
had God a thundercloud dark face
and God been born a slave.

He had raised himself as high as heaven,
as high as human dignity:
behold,
Frederick Douglass, *free!*

On the twisting road from slavery,
was there a manual menial job
that he had missed?
His hands had planted, hoed,
sawed wood,
shoveled coal,
carried dung,
dug cellars,
shined shoes,
swung a crane,
wielded bellows,
rolled barrels of oil,
hauled cargo,
hoisted his weight and more in sweat, in pain, in pride.

What he held inside his hands no master could take away.

What you got there boy?
Open your fist and show.

Nothing, sir.

Don't try no trick now boy.
Give it to me quick.

The hands forced open wide
showed nothing inside.
Merely blisters, scars, cuts,
a bloodhound's bite
from an early runaway day,
welts from master's whip,
slip of the knife,
gash, lash, scab,
an oozing sore,
but dark blood can't hurt
the same as white,
so there was nothing there,
no special sight . . .

All right boy.
I see there's nothing.
Get on with your chores.

                  Alone, he would cup his hands
                  and stare at his secret.
                  Without shape or form
                  and colorless as water,
                  invisible as air,
                  he could feel it all the same—
                  alive, pulsing, warm.
                  It was all he had,
                  but it was all his own:
                  what could one call it?
                  It was himself, his entity:
                  a wish, a will, a dare:
                  its name was *free*
                  and it was always there.

The sky above the head of a slave
Is the sky above a deep deep grave.
Nothing but dirt and stone and endless night.
No horizon for you to sight.
The way you're born,
that's the way you stay,
and the only release
is Judgment Day.
Tears dry up and leave no stain.
And what's one more cry in a world of pain?

Cornmeal,
ashcake,
cold clay floor.
Work
till you drop
and then
work some more.

And every sensible master knows
how to keep Uncle Tom and good old Mose.

Let them sing and let them pray
and track down every runaway.

You'll hardly need to tighten the chains
if you just make sure they don't use their brains.

    A pail of water
    and a nosebag of feed,
    and don't let them learn
    to write or read.
    Just that sloppit of water
    and a big enough crumb
    to keep them alive

and keep them *dumb*.

A slave's to fetch,
a slave's to bring,
a slave's not a person:
a slave's a thing.

A piece of kindling,
like wood to burn,
and a piece of wood's
got no need to *learn*.

A slave's a field
to plow and sow;
step on a field
and it won't even know.

A field's just dirt
where seeds can grow
and the place of a field
is down below.

The sky above the head of a slave
is the sky above a deep deep grave.
How to make a breakaway?
How to tunnel through night to the light of day?

Dig a hole deeper into the ground?
No matter how deep, soon be found.

Have to aim higher for freedom's flight:
aim to learn how to read and write.

Master, master,
beware young Fred:
revolution
in his head!

Master's wife starting
the boy on his way;
shows him the Bible
and what the words say.

Master comes by
and takes it away.

Then whip him until
the boy is half-dead;
but all that he's read
stays safe in his head.

Take away one book,
he finds another;
learns dangerous words
like *helper* and *brother*.

And his favorite word
like a high-flying bird
over the sea
is *free*.
F as in *Frederick*.
F as in *Free*.

Now horrors, now Hades,
new frightening sight:
grabbed onto a pencil—
he's starting to write!

He'd get by on water
and a crust of bread,
but his mind was starving
to be fed.

Where there was a book,
there was Fred:

books at his workbench,
books in his bed.

Letters of the alphabet
each like a root
reaching to a tree
bearing freedom fruit.

Learning the marks,
funny squiggly lines
untangling to grow
into freedom signs.

How beautiful those dark lines of writing came to be:
and most beautiful of all—
spelling *Frederick Douglass, free.*

〰

How long ago,
how very long ago.

Slavery and the Civil War
were ancient history—
or partly so.

Now here he was, with hair as white as snow.
On this platform today
to support the rights of women,
the rights of labor,
free education for all;
exhorting the end
of every kind of slavery
that remained
to hold the human mind enchained.

The hall rocked with applause
as the women delegates in unison
waved their handkerchiefs,
little white sailboats
timidly bravely setting out upon
the thundercloud dark sea.
He was that great dark sea,
eternal Frederick Douglass,
freedom's forward tide,
never to be contained.

That evening he died.

Farewell, farewell,
toll the cold iron bell.
Black mourning crepe draping Douglass Hall.
The marble statue remote and classic-browed.
The flag lowered to half-mast.
Judges and senators filing past

to see the great man lying in state.
Grieving, the crowd of mourners came
and came and came
in stumbling waves of disbelief.

> That majestic white-maned head
> no longer to be lifted high?
> His passionate words no more
> to blaze against the sky?
> How could the great dark father ever say goodbye?

> Then bitterly rejoice
> that only death
> could still his freeman's voice.

> And with it gone,
> that others echo on:

> that myriad
> dear dark
> sons and daughters
> embark
> upon the future's
> unknown boundless waters.

Henry Thoreau

It's American to celebrate
the Fourth of July
with fireworks
and brass bands
and blueberry pie,
with flags and a parade;
and after lemonade
has washed the speeches down,
it's time to go back home
to your house in town.
Hoorah for these United States,
and throw away the paper plates.

But in eighteen forty-five,
on Independence Day,
Henry Thoreau of Concord
chose a different way.
Packed up all his worldly goods
and moved from town into the woods.
How super-independent,
how positively rude
to go and leave your neighbors
in search of solitude.

What an odd one was Henry,
what a strange, wild stray!

Lived there for two years and more
in every kind of season.
Folks in Concord town
couldn't figure out the reason.

Snow and ice and thaw and flood;
wind and drought and bugs and mud . . . !

Henry'd been in business,
he'd even taught school;
wouldn't have thought
he'd turn out such a fool.

What could he learn
by camping out alone?
He'd surely earn no money,
and there'd be nothing he could *own*.

But even back at Harvard
Henry had been queer:
wore that one green homespun suit
all around the year.
A little wiry fellow,
didn't look so strong;
seemed more like an Indian
the way he nosed along . . .

His blue-gray eyes
peering down at the ground,
as though some secret was waiting to be found.
With his beat-up boots
and his uncut hair,
he was hardly a model
for the neat town square.

Off went Henry
on Independence Day
with a borrowed axe
and a flute to play.
Whack, thwack,
he'd give the axe back;
but the music
was his to stay.

Built himself a house
out of fresh white pine:
only ten feet wide,
but the view was fine:
look, straight downhill
from his open door—

there was Walden Pond
and the curving shore!
He put in two windows,
a few supplies and stores,
and when friends came by to visit
(or snoopy sniffy bores)
they sat in his "best" parlor—
the grass outdoors.

Henry lived a life there
singular as could be;
one desk, one bed, one table,
but of chairs—a crowd of three:
one for solitude,
two for friendship,
and the third allowed for
"society".

The pond gave him water
clear and sweet,
driftwood for fire,
and fish to eat.
The pond was his outlook,
the pond was his fate,
the pond was his bountiful
rich estate.
The pond gave him white sand
to scrub his floor,
the pond gave him nature's

horizon and more:
squawkings of fish-hawks,
laughing of loons,
mornings of mist
and reflections of moons.

He hoed his bean-garden,
he read and he wrote
(with always time out
for a wood thrush's note).
Like a deer or a fox,
he knew the woods through
(and each day for hours
admired all anew).

Blueberries in summer
and corn growing high,
and woodchucks and children
scampering by.
Then maples turned scarlet
in the cool fall;
he built a chimney
and plastered the wall.

Geese flew south,
and the pond froze hard;
he skated across
his smooth winter "yard".

The melting snow
began to roar,
and ferns and cattails
sprang up once more.

(Of all the scenes
he came to know,
he loved the most
the Spring coming slow . . .)

The fields moist and bare,
still icicles there,
then faint as a snowflake
a song in the air—!
The marsh quakes,
the frog wakes,

the brooks tumble and spill,
and suddenly grass
flames up on the hill:
fire of desire
that can never be spent.
And so the seasons came and went.

It wasn't wholly
a Paradise:
there were briars and thorns,
and his crops failed twice.
There were times when his mind
felt blank as the snow
and he longed for the sound
of a human echo;
he'd row far out
in his boat and shout
just so a word could be heard.

Yet always the creatures and seasons came back,
and the woods were his again to track
and the dome of the sky was his home.

So he found the great world
in a small inland beach,
and he learned the lesson
that none can teach,
that each of us
must strive to reach:

he learned to love darkness
as well as light,
and he learned to see
with a natural sight
that fish and bird and man are one
with the earth and the sea and the stars and the sun.

Lucretia
Mott

What sort of tether
could hold them together:
impulsive Lucretia
and halting James?
Sea captain's daughter from Nantucket Island,
salty, adventurous all of her days,
and young Mr. Mott
with his set mainland ways.

What was the bonding,
strong as steel   supple as leather,
to keep such an unlikely couple together?

So unlike in every trait:
slate-eyed and dark-haired, tiny Lucretia;
towering, tow-headed, blue-eyed James.

Lucretia whose tongue could never be still;
James for whom all speech was always uphill.

With quick-as-a-trick Lucretia,
with James
so
ploddingly
slow—
what sort of life could the two of them share?

As if the tortoise and the hare
were to make a married pair!

Upon their April wedding day,
Lucretia garbed in sober gray,
just a flicker of white for her kerchief and cap.
The ceremony plain as could be
with Quaker phrasing of *thy* and *thee:*
on the meeting house bench they sat
side by side, gazing straight ahead;
then, at a simple command, they rose
hand in hand, faced each other
and pledged their future life:
sat down again as husband and wife.

It couldn't last,
they were so wrongly matched
from the very start;
temperamentally
poles apart.

The parade of nay-sayers
brayed and nayed:
Lucretia's fire would have to damp down,
for the coolness of James could never change.
Or the rock of James would be chipped away
by the snip of a needle-sharp girl.

One of them would have to give in:
which of the two would win?
Stubborn Lucretia or stalwart James?
Stalwart Lucretia or stubborn James?
All that they shared was their pairing of names.

Darting Lucretia, deliberate James:
opposite natures, identical aims.
Bride and groom
from the very start
sharing a unified will and heart.

> *Oppose injustice by every non-violent means.*
> *Simple as a song,*
> *that was their refrain life-long.*

A test came soon.
They scarcely had a honeymoon
before a time of trial.

James was due to take his turn at military service.
It was merely routine,
a harmless chore;
the country in no way threatened by war.

He was a Quaker, a pacifist.
He would not go.

But wasn't it quixotic to resist?

Advice came to James from every side.
Why risk imprisonment and blacklist?
Even throughout the Quaker Society of Friends,
not every member kept harmony between all means and ends.
Be a man of peace—but not fanatically.

Only James could not be satisfied.
Stubbornly, he held to his creed,
and stalwartly, Lucretia agreed.

His jail sentence lasted a mere two days.
The principle clear for always.
    Beyond the laws
    there could come a more sacred cause.
    If need be,
    he would break the laws of men again.
    And so would she.

Conscience that called with an inner voice
bound them also to love and rejoice.

Mother Lucretia, Father James:
blessed with babies abundantly
babbling, reaching, crying and cooing,

crawling, falling, chewing, *doing*. . . .

In an age when parents rarely smiled,
the Motts delighted in every child.
Unorthodox in everything,
they taught their children to pray—and sing.

> What a heretic household
> where it was understood
> that children weren't always
> expected to be good!

> How strange not to treat children
> like objects on display,
> not to serve them up for company
> like teacups on a tray,
> and then when you had had enough—
> to order them away.

> What a peculiar family,
> that family of Mott
> caring more for one another
> than a broken toy or spot;
> a most peculiar family,
> caring more to keep their consciences
> clear of any blot.

James was selling cotton cloth,
a good livelihood;

while they didn't bask in riches,
they did moderately well
till Lucretia had to ask:
> How was cotton grown?
> Wasn't the answer only too well known?

> *White white cotton in the Southern sun*
> *black seeds in the cotton in the golden sun*
> *deeper and deeper the blood-red sun*
> *tighter and tighter the cotton thread spun. . . .*

They must give up their ill-gotten trade,
and never again deal in anything slave-made.
This time it was stubborn Lucretia who decreed
and James who stalwartly agreed.
Furthermore, they took a vow:
from now on there would not be
anything in their own home
that came from where
people were held as property.
That meant no more sugar from the canefield South;
molasses instead from islands far away at sea,
and calico cloth from Quaker farms on North Carolina land—
all else was contraband—
when the family Mott
began to boycott
they did it totally:
the only products that they would buy
must all be "free".

Nothing slave-made ever use:
exhorting others to share their views,
Lucretia spoke up more and more in meeting.
(Among the Quakers, women did not have to be
shyly retiring or retreating.)

⊛

Lucretia moved steadily forward.
Became an official preacher.
Before her passionate voice and piercing eyes,
it was hard to maintain a sanctimonious guise:
that the law is the law . . . rules are made to be obeyed. . . .
Lucretia thundered: humanity comes first,
thou durst not be afraid!

Spoke until her voice grew hoarse,
then turned the force of her argument
to silent picketing or writing;
engaging in every form of non-violent fighting.
Looking gentle, demure in her Quaker gray,
she used every minute of every day;
if sitting, she'd be knitting—a scarf with a freedom slogan,
and every birthday card, greeting, invitation
that busy little body sent
went intertwined with abolitionist sentiment.

Her deeds were trivial and great,
silly and superb.
Did housework, hackwork, holy work,
believing truly that all men were her brothers,
and women of every color and kind her sisters,
this little lady preacher,
this most belligerent of non-resisters.

With all her activity,
she needed a sanctuary,
a place of deliberate calm,
some haven for the heart
where she could be apart from outside claims.
Remember James?
Supporting Lucretia in all her public acts,
abetting her passion with logic and with facts.
Lucretia was ready to speak anywhere;
James would carefully drive her there.
In their Dearborn wagon the duo would go;
he'd cover her up with a laprobe of fur
and watch out for the road, for the weather, for her.
She was still gabby, nimble, and spry.
He was still gawkily solemn and shy.
They didn't change much as the years went by.
They still thought as *we* and never *I*.

He knew how hard it was for her to hide
her natural angry pride.
She knew that though her opinions could be swayed,

once James had made his mind up, there it stayed.
Most of all, she knew he kept her unafraid.
In letters she spoke of "James and self"
as if the two were an integer.

Darting Lucretia, deliberate James:
opposite natures, identical aims;
sharing a unified will and heart,
though by temperament still wide apart.
Out in the garden, he'd hoe and weed;
she'd rather sew by the fire and read.
He preferred a straightback chair;
it was hard for her to sit still anywhere,
but at least a rocker could go to and fro. . . .

    So unalike in every way,
    their marriage could hardly last a day——

    ——enduring all kinds of emotional weather
    together for fifty-seven years.

On their golden anniversary,
what a merry Mott time was had by all!
James, though white-haired and bent, still tall,
and Lucretia, though fragile, so *powerfully* small.
Children, grandchildren, friends by the score,
and a sense of what life was worth living for:
always the sacred cause
above any man-made laws.

James and Lucretia,
unquenchable flames,
indelibly linked
their lives and names.

Whichever of the two died first:
worse to be the one living.

Lucretia was left
inconsolable, bereft.
James was gone.
James was gone.
Her heart and soul were dead;
if only her body had also fled.
James was gone!

But nature, as it has to,
comes yearly to renew.
Spring was coming on,
time of their April wedding.
Flowers began to appear:
yellow forsythia,
crocus,
jonquil golden as
their golden fifty years.
A granddaughter had planned to be wed
on just that anniversary date.
(But that was before Grandfather James was dead.)
Now it would be blasphemous;
their wedding must wait
for a less heartbreaking day in late summer or fall.

Lucretia dried her tears.
The wedding should take place
on exactly the date as planned.
James and self would have it so.
Let there be no doubt about it.
The color came back to her face
as the preacher in her took over:
let their long-lived years together
be an omen of clear and sunny weather
for this new bride and groom.
There was nothing about the past to mourn;
time for rejoicing, time to be reborn.

After the wedding,
Lucretia came home and took off her bonnet and cheerful smile.
The world seemed so quiet since James had died.
She glanced outside.
There was a rustling breeze blowing across those two trees
he had planted from acorns years before.
Lucretia sighed. Like James, they had rooted deep and true.
Suddenly, there was something she wanted to do.

James had helped to found a different kind of school
that went not by the flogging stick and rule,
but by the radical theory
that children should be taught humanely.
Lucretia had the trees transplanted to the school nearby.
She was pleased to see them grow strong and high,
not a dead statue,
but a living memorial to James.
Stalwart oaks, in autumn their leaves
holding on long after the scarlet and gold
of maples and birches had gone.
Their copper tones
Like James. Not flamboyant, but stalwart.
Not easily swayed.

How dear were the years they had had!
Suddenly, she could live more easily
with memory
and face the dark and winter cold
alone.

Later, after Lucretia died,
was it only a dazzlement
made by the sun and shade,
or could it be so
that the twin trees
planted side by side
had come to grow
into one arching splendor against the sky?

Ida B.
Wells

Holly Springs in Mississippi
was a pretty little place
with Spanish moss growing
as soft as lace,
with glossy magnolias
and songbirds in trees,
with juleps and jasmine
in the sweet evening breeze,
with dusty back roads
and garden-front streets,
with parasols and fans
and the Klan in sheets.

With one season's gain
and another's losses
and some nights lit up
by fiery crosses,
Holly Springs was the picture
of a pleasant Southern town,
and Ida B. was born there
beautiful and brown.

Sweet as a blossom
on a peach tree,
there she was—
lovely
for all to see.

It was a pleasure
to watch her go by

with her delicate figure
and sudden smile,
and always dressed
in the daintiest style;
Ida B., Ida B.,
so graceful to see
with her diamond-bright eyes
and soft hair piled high.

But something was wrong
with sweet Ida B.
There it was
plain
for all to see
and it was a worry
to watch her go by:
    that girl looked everyone straight in the eye.
    That girl didn't mumble, she opened her mouth:
    didn't she know that the South was the South?

    Young Ida B.,
    beware,
    beware:
    trouble
    will come
    if
    you
    don't
    have

a
care!

Ida B. took trouble in her stride.
Only fourteen when both parents died.
Four younger brothers and sisters to tend,
homework and housework and cook clean and mend:
it looked like a long road that never would bend . . .
But Ida B. managed to provide.

She finished with school
and started to teach,
but kept reaching out
for
what wasn't in reach.

Ida B.,
Ida B.,
bound
to
declare,
more trouble
will come

if
you
don't
have
a
care!

Why can't you lock up the thoughts in your heart?
Must you always speak out just the way that you feel?
When will you learn that
real
and
ideal
(like the two races)
are far apart?

  Ida B.,
  Ida B.,
  please have a care;
  trouble's just looking for someone to share—
  you'll be
  that someone,
  now
  be
  aware!

Ida B. moved
from the small 'Sippi town
and everyone hoped that
she'd soon settle down.

Memphis was bigger
than Holly Springs,
and yet she found there
the very same things.
The streets and the sidewalks
were smooth and wide,
but a Negro still had to step aside.
The mockingbirds sang
as back home they'd sung,
and sometimes from lamp posts
dark shadows were flung
just as magnolias
had heavily hung
when some special weight
on the branches
swung . . .

Ida B. couldn't learn
to hold her tongue.

     Ida. B.,
     Ida B.,
     won't you take care?
     Can't you accept

that life is unfair?
Besides,
it's a stranger,
you don't know the man.
Go home and prepare
tomorrow's lesson plan.
You're getting by,
why look around?
Trouble's just aching
to be found.

But Ida B. walked with her head held high,
and persisted in staring life straight in the eye.

The subjects she taught seemed less vital each day.
She was earning more in Memphis on her teacher's pay;
Each month she put a part of it away.
Saved and saved
for what she craved. . . .

      . . . now do you suppose
      she wanted a castle
      or carriage
      or clothes?
      To be bowed to,
      kowtowed to,
      satined and velveted,
      silkened and plushed?

      You know her by now:

it was not to be hushed.
Ida B. had a dream, and she scrimped for the day:
if she owned a newspaper,
she'd have her own way;
then none could blue-pencil,
she'd speak her own say!

By the age of only twenty-three,
the dream of Ida B.
became reality.

Now she could teach what she wanted to teach
in her weekly paper:
the *Memphis Free Speech,*
for she was the editor
(the co-owner, too)
and could print all the news
from her own point of view.

Wasn't it shockingly long past time
for lynching to be counted a major crime?
Mobs went unpunished for their attacks.
—Because the victims were usually blacks?
—Was that why the guilty kept getting off free?
Dangerous questions from Ida B.

Dear Ida B.,
please don't crusade;
why can't you be
just a little afraid?

If you have to protest,
write of things far away.
Don't interfere
with what's
here
every day!

Condemn the tyrants of ancient Rome
(don't mention the sheriffs so close to home.)
Indict abstract evils with your pen—
and not our local businessmen.

Ida B. was human—
of course she was scared.
But being Ida B.,
the truth wasn't spared.

Three young Negro men were lynched one night.
It was clear enough, there was plenty of light
to see the faces of violence and hate.
Ida B. didn't stop to hesitate.

She did what she knew was bound to enrage.
She went and named names on her paper's front page.

Not only the names of the red-necked mob,
but the "gentlemen" who had incited the "job"—
the men of means
behind the scenes
who were whitely polite

and oh so nice
and quiet as ice.
—And who didn't like the competition
of Negroes aspiring to *their* position.

       Ida B., Ida B.,
       too late to beware;
       now trouble's lunging from everywhere!
       Hear the howling voices?
       The stamping feet?
       They're coming closer—
       they're right on your street!
       The torches are blazing!
       They're up the stair!

They burned down her office.
Smashed the press.
And they'd have got to
Ida B. unless—

   —friends came to rescue her just in time.
   Or there'd have been one more lynching crime.

     Ida B.,
     Ida B.,
     Ida begone,
     flee
     before
     the
     bloody
     dawn.

She couldn't go back to Tennessee,
but she kept on being Ida B.

Up North in Illinois, in Lincoln's own state
the number of lynchings still was great.
No one knew how many each year
were murdered by mobs in hysterical fear.

65

No one had ever kept records before.
Ida B. tallied up the terrible score.

And rather than praying to change some natures,
she campaigned for Negroes in legislatures.
Instead of kindly sympathy,
she believed in action,
did Ida B.
It was good to have faith in a worthy cause,
but better to pass—and enforce—the laws.

She became a crusading editor's wife,
and went on enjoying the rest of her life:
organized women in clubs, and lectured to youth,
and kept agitating
to print the truth.
Stayed pretty as ever,
with her head held high
and kept on looking
life
straight
in
the
eye.

> *Clearly outspoken*
> *with head held high,*
> *and always looking life straight in the eye.*

Fiorello H. LaGuardia

What's New York?

Towers
rising
up.

A hole in the ground.

People boxed in
with concrete walls
around.

Elevator crush. Subway rush.
Push, poke, shove 'em in,
pack one more into the sardine tin.

Fire engines clang.
                    Garbage trucks bang.
Honk honk squawk squawk beep beep skureech
YIKES HEY Whynchamove outathe way?
Say, what's going on?

Just an ordinary day
here in Big Town, USA.

Who can stand it?
Who can hand it out and take it?
Who's got enough of the stuff to make it?

68

Only the toughest kind of fellow—
someone who's unmild   unmeek   unmellow—
in short:
a Fiorello!

Someone who's too dumb
                              or too smart
                                                to know the score
that when a contract is assigned,
can a bribe be far behind?

Someone who's too timid or too bold
to know just how
to kowtow to the dealers,
the wheelers and ward-heelers,
the mixers and fixers,
the politics and dirty tricks,
the bankroll bosses and the two-bit crime
that everybody winks at most of the time. . . .

. . . till along came this bobo, this Fiorello fellow
with a high squeaky voice instead of a bellow.
(What kind of leader or hero can he be
if he can't even speak with bass profundity?)
Sounds like a squirrel or a scolding bumble bee.
Feisty little guy. Built low to the ground.
Like a footstool. Like a mushroom. Like his name means "Little
                                                                        Flower",
and this Little Flower's punch packs a whale of power.

At his fullgrown height, five feet two
(Napoleon, move over, company for you.)
Even in his youth he'd take on every dare,
stand up and fight for what he thought was right,
and when his fists couldn't reach—
he'd stand up on a chair.

Fee, fi, fo, fo,
Fiorello, go, go, go.
But don't go in for too much reform,
not if you want to stay alive and warm.
Look at him taking on Tammany Hall!
Man, he's just begging for a fall!
He's down, he's out . . . no, he's back on his feet;
why won't the bullhead admit that he's beat?
A sentimental *googoo,* who's for good government,
who won't take a payoff, not a single red cent!

Where'd he come from, this prickly cactus flower?
Where'd he get the grit and the staying power?
What's his family pedigree?

    A polyglot,
    a melting pot:

Italian immigrants' American son,
an ecumenical council all rolled into one
—background Catholic atheist Protestant Jew—
speaking German Italian Hungarian French
Croatian Yiddish *un poco* Spanish too;
born in a New York tenement,
then spent
his boyhood in Arizona:
an international what's what, that's who!

Stenographer by day. Law school at night.
Opened an office as adviser to the poor,
his opinions about everything one hundred per cent sure.
Landlords Are Wrong. The People Are Right.
Join a union or the bosses will skin you raw;
see F. H. La Guardia, counsellor-at-law.
Never any doubt about which side was which:
angels' haloes for the poor folks,
devil's pitchforks for the rich.

Fee, fi, fo, fo, Fiorello go, and *go!*
Shock of dark hair rumpled over his eye,
big black sombrero and a skinny string tie.
Walked so fast he all but ran,
Mister Miniature Superman.

Everything always on the broadest scale:
he'd win every case—well, maybe once in a while
he just *might* fail . . .

If he had a fault, it wasn't over-modesty.
"When I make a mistake, it's a beaut," said he.

Played the cornet, and was never afraid
to toot his own horn from the day he was born.

Time to turn the rascals out, put the people in power;
and he'd been born at just the right hour.

But how do you go ahead and win elections?
How convince the voters that you're heaven-sent
to represent them in government?
Especially when you don't have connections,
and your bank account is hardly overflowing?

Go, Fiorello, go, go, go,
practice campaigning, and keep horn-blowing!

> Smart and sassy as a shiny brass band
>   —oompah oompah, take note of Fiorello,
>   oompah, oompah, vote for the fellow—

it didn't turn out exactly as planned.

You couldn't make it up, this fantastic true story
of pluck and luck,
of accident and intentional glory.

The scene really happened, it's not a movie screen:
a Republican clubhouse, nineteen hundred and fourteen;
all the pros of the regular political machine
were lining up candidates for their slate—
a humid summer night, and the hour was late—
they fanned themselves in the airless air
(some brand new club member was also there).

"Who wants to run for Congress?" the district leader asked.
A yawn and a pause, then grins and guffaws.
The joke was an old one, understood by all;
what patsy would they put up against Tammany Hall?
It was a leadpipe cinch that the Democrats would win,
but—purely formality—a name should be put in.
Who'd choose to be the candidate most likely to lose?

"I want to run,"
said someone.
        Who
        in the insane asylum
        are you?
            "La Guardia. Fi-o-rell—"

Oh, let's get a name that at least we can spell.

"I'll tell it to you loud and clear.
FIORELLO H. LA GUARDIA."

They spelled it wrong.
But what did it matter if they didn't get it straight,
it still went along with the regular slate.
("Flullo La Guardia" it was marked down;
just another nonentity getting lost in Big Town.)
At meetings the candidates all got introduced—
except some square little fellow there in the back row
wearing a black sombrero.

Fiorello got mad. *He* could spell his own name.
He could yell it, too.
He bought a beat-up secondhand car

(the only kind that he could afford)
and plastered it with signs
like a mobile billboard:
"F. H. La Guardia For Congress,"
all around the district he'd go
starring in his one-man political show.
When the regular meetings and speeches were through
and the crowd was starting to drift away—
he'd zoom up in his car, jump out and get them to stay
by talking fast and loud till his face turned blue.
He'd rant and rave, he'd stamp and wave,
holler against the rich man's dollar,
and people laughed because the show was good—
and he got to know the neighborhood.
Went to christenings
               weddings
                       funerals
                               wakes

bar mitzvahs
           picnics
                street fairs
                     clambakes;
ate smoked eel, hot dogs, lasagna, gefilte fish
and washed it all down with a potato knish.

Rang doorbells and climbed up stairs,
sat on packing boxes and kitchen chairs,
spoke the language of foreign lands,

shook thousands and thousands of workworn hands.

Election Day came!
               And as expected,
the Tammany Democrat got elected.

       But wait. Something was wrong
       with their usual sweet song.
       It had always been a landslide victory before;
       now they'd tallied up a barely winning score:
       their man just managing to get by—
       almost beaten out by that runty little guy.
       That boob of a cube had nearly got in;
       the upstart zero all but had a win!

       Better keep an eye on that bouncing pipsqueak fellow!
       And somebody find out how to spell Fiorello . . .

He'd pulled off a most improbable stunt:
lost the election, but wound up in front.

And the next time he won.

Fee, fi, fo, fo,
Fiorello on the go:
Congressman La Guardia in Washington.
Now he was really on his way;
a medium-big-shot from Big Town, U.S.A.

He served seven terms, until Tammany Hall
really pinned him against the wall.
La Guardia out. Their man in.
What kind of future and fame was left to win?
He wasn't as young as he once had been.
At fifty the legs don't run upstairs so fast;
maybe his political days were all past. . . .

The time was nineteen thirty-three,
a time of plenty—
of poverty.
So back to campaigning and corner speaking,
his voice still indignant and still high-squeaking.
People need jobs! Cut the red tape! Fire all the crooks!
Make the city government open up its books!
Go after the grafters, and clear out the known racketeers!
His speeches brought on laughter and cheers—

and votes from the consumer and the poor tax-payer:
enough to elect him
His Honor the Mayor.

    Now what shall we do with an honest mayor,
    what shall we do with an upright mayor,
    what shall we do with a do-good mayor
    in Big Town, U.S.A.?
        Throw the bum out.
        Unfair to organized crime.
        He's sweeping the dirt out from everywhere!
        This loony buffoon doesn't know when to stop—
        he's even policing every cop!

So what can we do with an honorable,
an upright type, a holy terror,
an open-hander, a spotlight-stander
here in Big Town, U.S.A.?

Keep him in as long as he'll stay:
the one-man circus, the workhorse clown,
who turned New York City upside down:
who slew the dragon of Tammany Hall,
a man of peculiar sentiment
demanding accounting from one and all
whenever public funds were spent
since it was the people's money
                    —wasn't he funny?—

Fiorello,
fabulous fellow,
Mayor of Big Town, U.S.A.:
elected three times with wild acclaim
Hooray *Hooray* HOORAY!
—And everybody learned how to spell his name.